Walk Around

M4 Sherman

By Jim Mesko

Color by Don Greer and Richard Hudson

Illustrated by Richard Hudson

MW00610748

Armor Walk Around Number 1

squadron/signal publications

Introduction

The M4 General Sherman tank was one of the great weapons of World War Two. While other tanks were better armed or carried thicker armor, the Sherman's reliability, speed, ease of maintenance, and adaptability made it the ideal vehicle to equip the US and Allied tank formations. The US, capitalizing on its broad automotive base, was able to produce over 30,000 M4s in five major subtypes. Additionally, the M4 served as the basis for a number of tank destroyers, self propelled-artillery, and specialty vehicles. Throughout its production life, the M4 underwent continual improvements in its armor, main gun, tracks and suspension, and internal equipment. Many of these improvements were introduced on the production line with minimal disruption. Many of the main components were interchangeable even though hundreds of companies were involved in the manufacturing of the component parts and its final assembly. This made spare parts procurement and repair much easier than with any other tank of the war (with the possible exception of the Russian T34 which, in many ways, was comparable to the Sherman's design philosophy).

The origins of the M4 Sherman can be traced back to the M3 General Grant/Lee series of medium tanks, which had in turn, evolved from the M2/M2A1 medium tank. The first M4 variants produced were the M4 and M4A1 — the former having a welded hull while the latter had a cast hull. Both vehicles were equipped with gasoline-powered Continental radial engines. The M4A2 was powered by a General Motors diesel engine and employed an all welded hull. The M4A3 was fitted with a Ford GAA-V V-8 gasoline engine designed specifically for the M4 and also featured a welded hull. The M4A4 was powered by a Chrysler A57 multi-banked engine which required a slightly lengthened welded hull. All M4A4s were fitted with the early three-piece differential/final drive housing and most were shipped to the British under Lend-Lease, although some were used for training in the US. The designation M4A5 was assigned to the Canadian-built Ram series — developed out of the earlier M3 design, but bearing a superficial resemblance to the M4. The final variant, the M4A6, was basically an M4A4 hull fitted with the Caterpillar D200A, and later, the Ordnance RD-1820 engine. The M4A6 was easily distinguished by a large bulge on top the engine deck.

This brief description of the M4 production subtypes cannot even scratch the surface of the wide variations, which occurred throughout the production history of the Sherman. The final production M4s were only barely recognizable in lineage to the original M4s. Numerous changes in the hull, turret, suspension, and armament, along with minor changes in fittings, led to a vehicle that served in various foreign armies late into this century. In this respect, it again matches up with the Russian T34, another truly great weapon of World War Two. In the following pages, we will follow the detail evolution of the M4 General Sherman — one of the great weapons, which helped the Allies win World War II.

Acknowledgements

I would like to thank the following people without whom this book would not have been possible: Henry Venetta who gave freely of his time and two beautifully restored Shermans one very hot August day, Wayne Hlavin who helped flesh out obscure M4 details on short notice, Jacque Littlefield who gave me the run of his outstanding personal collection of AFV's, Mike Green who took special select photos which illustrated key M4 features, Richard Hunnicutt for his support throughout all my projects, and especially Duane Ward who took the vast majority of these photos on that very hot day in August at Henry Venetta's museum and without whose help this book would not have been possible. To all of you a heartfelt thanks.
Photo Credits:
U.S. Army, National Archives, and Patton Armor Museum

Dedication:

To Rusty and Judy for two great years of leadership and support. May the years to come be even better and more productive for all of us.

COPYRIGHT 2000 SQUADRON/SIGNAL PUBLICATIONS, INC.
1115 CROWLEY DRIVE CARROLLTON, TEXAS 75011-5010
All rights reserved. No part of this publication may be reproduced, stored in a retrieval system or transmitted in any form by means electrical, mechanical or otherwise, without written permission of the publisher.

ISBN 0-89747-410-4

If you have any photographs of aircraft, armor, soldiers or ships of any nation, particularly wartime snapshots, why not share them with us and help make Squadron/Signal's books all the more interesting and complete in the future. Any photograph sent to us will be copied and the original returned. The donor will be fully credited for any photos used. Please send them to:

Squadron/Signal Publications, Inc.
1115 Crowley Drive
Carrollton, TX 75011-5010

Если у вас есть фотографии самолётов, вооружения, солдат или кораблей любой страны, особенно, снимки времён войны, поделитесь с нами и помогите сделать новые книги издательства Эскадрон/Сигнал ещё интереснее. Мы переснимем ваши фотографии и вернём оригиналы. Имена приславших снимки будут сопровождать все опубликованные фотографии. Пожалуйста, присылайте фотографии по адресу:

Squadron/Signal Publications, Inc.
1115 Crowley Drive
Carrollton, TX 75011-5010

軍用機、装甲車両、兵士、軍艦などの写真を所持しておられる方はいらっしゃいませんか？どの国のものでも結構です。作戦中に撮影されたものが特に良いのです。Squadron/Signal社の出版する刊行物において、このような写真は内容を一層充実し、興味深くすることができます。当方にお送り頂いた写真は、複写の後お返しいたします。出版物中に写真を使用した場合は、必ず提供者のお名前を明記させて頂きます。お写真は下記にご送付ください。

Squadron/Signal Publications, Inc.
1115 Crowley Drive
Carrollton, TX 75011-5010

(Front Cover) An early production M4A1 rumbles ashore on the Normandy beachhead during the late morning hours of 6 June 1944. German panzers were few and far between — Allied armor concentrated on cleaning out German pockets of resistance.

(Previous Page) M4A3E8s are readied for movement to new positions in South Korea. The use of Russian-built T-34/85s by the North Koreans was a cause for some concern on the part of US and South Korean troops until heavier US armor — the M4, M26, and M46 — could be brought on line. The crew of the near Sherman has added logs to the hull sides for additional protection.

(Back Cover) An M4A3E8 of the 72nd Tank Battalion fires on North Korean positions in May of 1952. Despite the hilly and often rugged terrain of the Korean peninsula, US armor operations were generally successful.

The first M4 variant to be produced was the M4A1 — a vehicle fairly similar to the T6 prototype, albeit with the hull side hatches welded closed. The M4A1 featured the cast hull, one of the three basic hull variants used in the Sherman line. The M4A1 had smooth, rounded hull lines and gradual changes in the suspension and differential/final drive housing. (PAM)

The M4 employed the second type of hull — the welded version — which allowed a slight increase in ammunition storage and interior space. The hull featured flat sides, sharply angled corners, and a 60° glacis plate. Both the M4 and the M4A1 used the Continental R 975C1 engine. (PAM)

The last major hull style had the glacis plate inclined at a 47° angle compared to the 60° angle used on the earlier welded hulls. This was one of the more common models to be seen in US service following World War II. This particular model, the M4A3E8 employed the Horizontal Volute Spring Suspension (HVSS) system and was armed with a 76 MM gun.

The final hull variant was a combination of the cast glacis plate mated to a welded hull, fighting, and engine compartment. Known as the 'composite hull' the new hull was identical to this experimental M4E6 tested at Aberdeen Proving Grounds. This composite hull Sherman is also equipped with a 76 MM gun. (PAM)

3

The rounded appearance of the hull is evident in the front profile view. The driver and assistant driver protrusions — prominent on the early welded hulls — were smoothly faired into the cast hull.

The cast hull had no sharp angles, which could serve as shot traps. The hull surface had a rough surface due to the casting process. This particular M4A1 is a late production vehicle that was rebuilt in 1949.

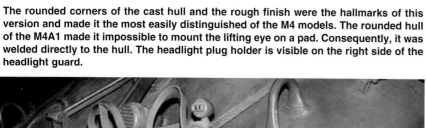

The rounded corners of the cast hull and the rough finish were the hallmarks of this version and made it the most easily distinguished of the M4 models. The rounded hull of the M4A1 made it impossible to mount the lifting eye on a pad. Consequently, it was welded directly to the hull. The headlight plug holder is visible on the right side of the headlight guard.

The only real indentation in the front of the cast hull was the hull machine gun mount. The machine gun was protected by a small rounded mantlet that surrounded the barrel. This type of hull was the largest single-piece casting manufactured at that time.

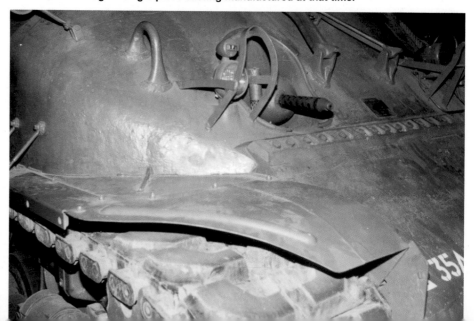

4

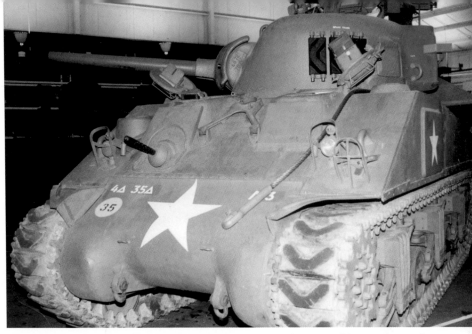

The early welded hulls featured a 60° slope to the front plate. The sharp slope of the glacis required the addition of armored boxes over the drivers' positions. Additional armor plates were welded on the sides to thicken the armor over the internal ammunition bins. This vehicle is also equipped with both open and solid spoked wheels — a not uncommon occurrence.

The box-like projections of the driver's and assistant driver's positions were weak points, since they compromised the integrity of a single flat front plate. When this became evident, additional armor plates were welded in front of the two positions.

The angular lines of the welded hull contrasted sharply with the smooth lines of the cast version. The welded hull — in a variety of sub-variants — was produced in the largest numbers of the two main hull types.

The number of potential shot traps in the welded hull compared to the cast hull was much greater, although the welded version did have more internal space for ammunition. Supplemental armor was also welded onto the hull sides to increase protection over the ammunition storage bins.

5

(Below) Compared to the other hull types, the front of this late production welded hull M4A3 was clean and uncluttered. The only exception to this was the indentation for the hull machine gun. Nevertheless, any protrusions — even small fittings — could cause problems if struck at the right angle by an incoming round.

(Above) The later type of welded hull featured a 47° front slope. The decreased angle eliminated the drivers' armored boxes built into the earlier 60° front plate. The new design provided additional space in the interior and improved the armor protection across the front of the vehicle.

(Below) Over the course of its design life, the M4 Sherman went through five different hull designs: cast and welded hulls, 60° sloped front armor to 47° armor, and a 'composite hull. The early cast hull M4A1 and its small turret and 75 MM gun is almost archaic looking when compared to this later welded hull M4A3E8 and its larger turret and gun.

6

M4 Hull Design

M4 (60° Glacis)

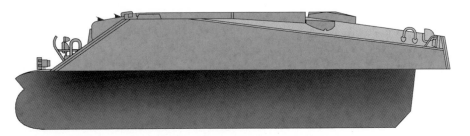

M4A1 (Early 60° Glacis)

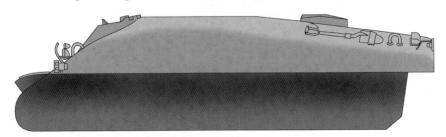

M4A1 (Late 47° Glacis)

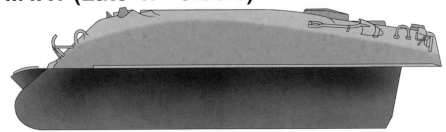

M4A2 (Late 47° Glacis)

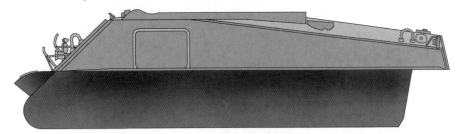

M4A3 (Early 60° Glacis)

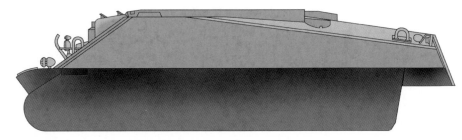

M4A3 (Late 47° Glacis)

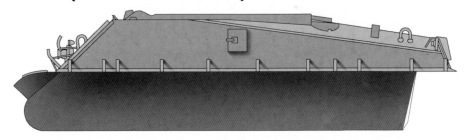

M4A4 (Early 60° Glacis and Long Hull)

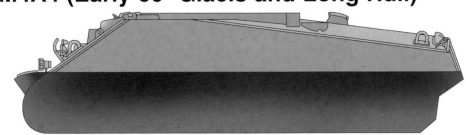

M4A6 (Late 47° Composite Long Hull

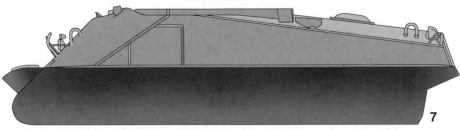

The original differential/final drive housing was a three-piece unit derived from that used on the M3 Grant/Lee medium tanks. The three pieces were bolted together. Unfortunately, the flanges used to bolt the pieces together provided convenient shot traps for German anti-tank weapons.

A single-piece cast unit was developed to eliminate the shot trap problem. Its general shape was similar to the three-piece unit, but it had a much more rounded shape and simplified construction. A strip of bolts along the top and bottom of the housing fastened the unit to the hull. A small crane was necessary to remove the housing and service the transmission and differential.

This version of the one-piece nose was more pointed and had thicker armor at its front. This unit was a common fitting on late production M4A3s. All of the differential housings were equipped with welded on towing eyes. Later variants, such as this one, were also equipped with crew steps.

The last common housing was similar to the second cast variant, but protruded more in front in addition to having a much sharper nose profile. The outwardly bulged ends covered the brake housings and were a common element on all of the final drive housings. This housing is fitted to an M10 Tank Destroyer which shared many chassis components with the M4.

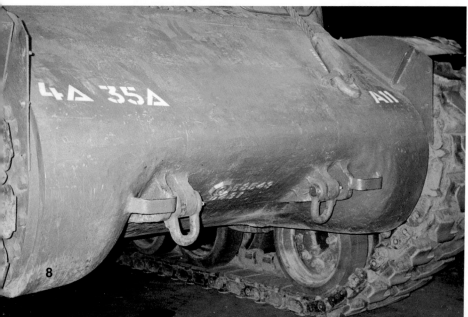

The front hull of an M4A3 shows the standard fittings associated with this version: from left to right are the lifting eye, antenna mount, headlight, hull machine gun, travel lock, headlight, lifting eye, and horn.

The right headlight was mounted just below the antenna mount on the front hull of this early M4A3. The small cylinder on the side of the light guard held the headlight socket plug when the headlight was not mounted. An antenna mount was built into the hull above the light.

Both the headlight guard and lifting eye have prominent weld seams. A blackout light was mounted on top of the main headlight. The light housings were screwed into sockets and could be removed and stored within the hull.

Another light, along with a horn, was mounted on the left side of the front hull. The horn is not mounted here; however, its cable conduit is barely visible behind the lower part of the guard. Early models carried the horn on the fender, but it was eventually relocated to the front hull.

The cable conduit was mounted on the right side of the horn. The holder and chain for the headlight plug are also visible on the right side of the headlight guard. A sheet metal fender was mounted immediately in front of the lights.

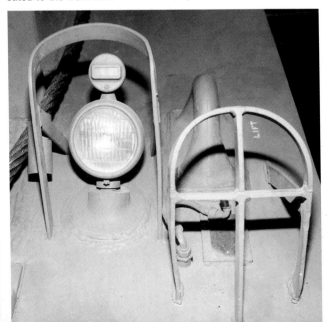

9

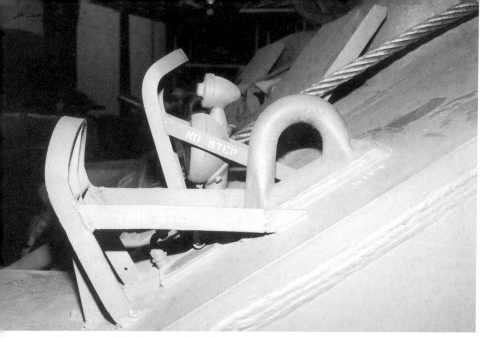

The angle of the horn and headlight guards was slightly different when viewed from the side. Also visible are the weld beads — built up in angled layers — on the lifting eye pad and the front plate where it meets the hull side.

The blackout light, standard on all Shermans, was mounted above the headlight. The headlight plug and chain are visible just above the machine gun barrel. The plug and chain ran beneath the headlight guard when in use. The opening of the machine gun port was protected by a cast mantlet slipped over the machine gun barrel.

The layout of this rebuilt M4A1 is slightly different from the M4A3: from the left are the lifting eye, headlight, hull machine gun, travel lock, horn, headlight, and another lifting eye. The barely visible drivers' rearview mirrors are mounted on both sides of the hull, although these were rarely carried in combat.

A lot number was cast into the lifting ring. Heavy weld beads characterized both the lifting eye and the headlight guards. Headlights and sirens/horn were easily damaged by small arms fire and shrapnel — replacements were usually stored within the hull. Both the lights and sirens could be unscrewed and easily replaced.

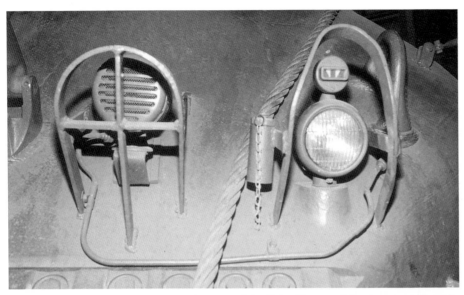

The horn on this M4A1 was mounted inboard of the light. The guard fronts were noticeably different from each other due to the need for light to be unobstructed — a requirement not needed with the horn.

There were at least two distinct types of horns used on the M4 series. This was the more common type used throughout the war.

Rearview mirrors, such as this one mounted on the side of an M4A1, were seen on some late production vehicles. Positioning the mirror required adjusting the bolts and screws to get the proper alignment. These were most often used for road or convoy travel. They were not normally used in combat since they were prone to damage.

Tubular fender supports helped hold the fenders to the hull. The lower part of the support was threaded and screwed into the upper portion. The weld attachment point is especially prominent on the side of the hull. Although side skirts were routinely fitted to Shermans, extended fenders were usually only seen on the later M4A3E8s equipped with the wider Horizontal Volute Spring Suspension (HVSS) system.

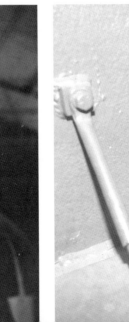

Late production M4s mounted spare track blocks on the hull side above the fenders. The track block was attached to the hull by a clasp, which had a semi-circular holder at each end. The bolt in the center was unscrewed to get the bolt out of the rack and release the clasp. The holes in the edge of the fender were used to mount the sheet metal sand shields. Spare tracks, carried in sufficient quantities, also provided a measure of protection against smaller anti-tank weapons.

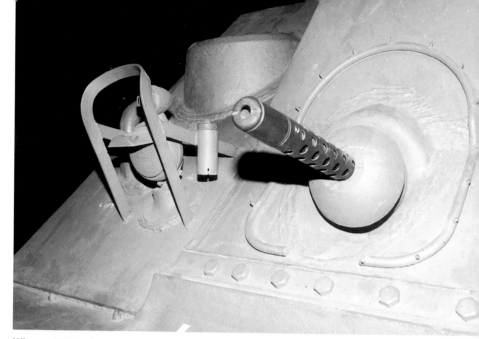

The M4 was fitted with a ball mounted, hand operated .30 caliber machine gun on the right side of the glacis plate. The weapon was fired by the assistant driver and used for suppressive fire and close-in defense. The weapon was not particularly accurate when the tank was in motion.

When additional armor was added to the front hull, the plate over the machine gun mount was modified to fit over the bulge caused by the ball mount. The tubular ring used to mount the fording and foul weather cover was also modified to fit over the new armor plate.

The machine gun had a limited traverse of fire of 20 degrees left and 25 degrees right — the lesser amount to the left being due to the proximity of the hull side. The assistant driver gauged the effectiveness of his fire by using tracers to 'walk' the rounds to the target.

The machine gun mount was protected by a small rounded mantlet with a flat face. A rubberized canvas cover was fitted over the gun and mount during inclement weather or when fording deep streams. The cover was snapped to the tubular ring surrounding the machine gun mount.

M4A1 (75) Sherman

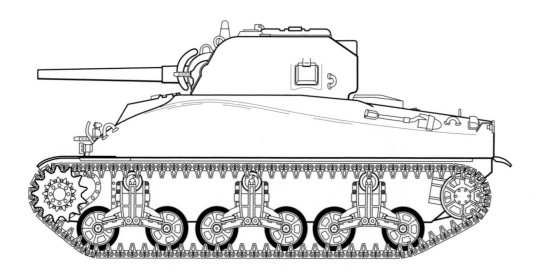

Specifications

Length: 19.1 Feet (5.84 м)
Width: 8.58 Feet (2.6 м)
Height: 9 Feet (2.74 м)
Weight (Empty): 62,700 lbs (28,441 кг)
Weight (Loaded): 66,800 lbs (30,300 кг)
Powerplant: Continental R975 C1, 400 hp
Transmission: Syncromesh, 5 speeds Forward, 1 Reverse
Speed: 24 mph (38.6 кмн)
Range: 120 miles (193 км)
Armament: 1 x 75mm Gun, 1 x .50 Caliber MG, 2 x .30 Caliber MG
Crew: 5

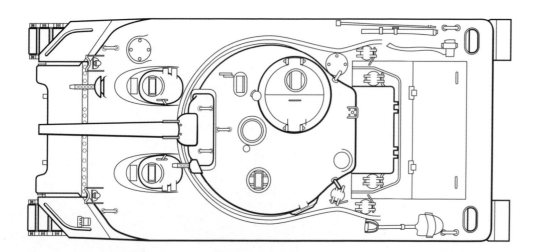

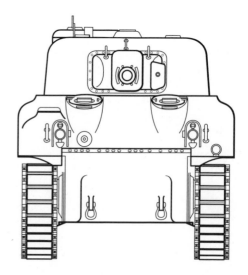

The Sherman used two principal types of suspension. The original type was known as the Vertical Volute Suspension System or VVSS. The first version of this type had the return roller mounted on top of the bogie housing. This unit was a carryover from the earlier M3 tank. This vehicle is also equipped with the early open-spoked idler wheel commonly found on Shermans throughout the war. The design was similar to that of the bogie wheel, however the idler wheel had six spokes instead of five. (PAM)

The suspension arms allowed the two road (or bogie) wheels to pivot with the rise and fall of the terrain. This early M3 bogie has been retrofitted with solid six-spoked road wheels. The return roller helped to guide the tracks as they made their way over the top of the suspension.

A second type of the VVSS unit featured a revised return roller arrangement and mounting bracket. The return roller was mounted on an arm behind the unit, while a top mounted skid helped to support the track. Although barely visible, the skid on this unit was symmetrically shaped in the form of a half circle. This unit was also known as the Heavy Duty VVSS.

M4 Bogie Assemblies

Middle Production

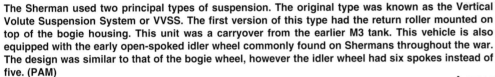

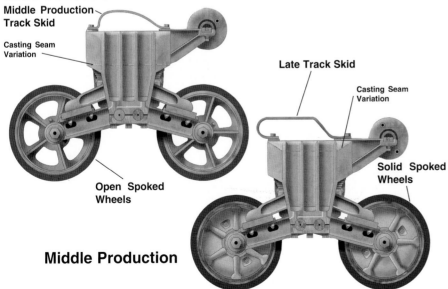

Middle Production Track Skid

Casting Seam Variation

Late Track Skid

Casting Seam Variation

Open Spoked Wheels

Solid Spoked Wheels

Middle Production

The basic bogie unit featured four vertical ribs on the face of the bogie housing, along with a series of casting marks. The return roller was initially mounted in line with the top of the arm. Later, a spacer was added to raise the return roller about an inch. This unit is equipped with the early open spoked wheels.

A third variation had the weld seam run across the bracket just above where it begins to angle inward. All four units on this page feature the late style track support skid on top of the bogie housing. This unit is equipped with the later stamped wheels.

A slight variation in the bogie housing had a weld seam angle down and then across the upper half of the unit. The bogie housings, suspension arms, and wheels were symmetrical and could be bolted to either side of the hull. Additional bolt holes allowed the track return roller arm and the track skid to be mounted on either side of the housing. This bogie unit is equipped with the later stamped wheels.

A more obvious change occurred late in production when the return roller arm was angled upward to further raise the height of the return roller. There were at least two variants of this, one with a weld seam (shown here) and one without an obvious seam. This unit is equipped with the early open spoke wheels covered by welded plates.

The straight return roller arm placed the roller in line with the skid. Later, a spacer was added to slightly raise the roller and provide additional support to the track. Properly supported and tensioned tracks were crucial to keeping them on the tank — especially during hard turns.

A raised return roller arm achieved the same result without the use of a spacer. Apart from the change in angle, the arms were identical in their design. Two sets of bolts secured the arm to the bracket. The upper set of bolts also anchored the rear of the skid to the top of the bogie housing.

The spacer (or pillow block) was basically the same shape as the end of the mount and fit into the recess. A longer screw was used to secure the unit to the arm.

The second type of M4 suspension was the Horizontal Volute Spring Suspension (HVSS). Two sets of paired wheels were attached to a single levered arm. Each arm could pivot independently of the other. A shock absorber and oil reservoir tank was mounted above the suspension arms. The volute springs were mounted horizontally beneath the shock absorber. The HVSS unit provided a better ride, while the wider tracks reduced ground pressure and provided improved flotation over soft ground.

17

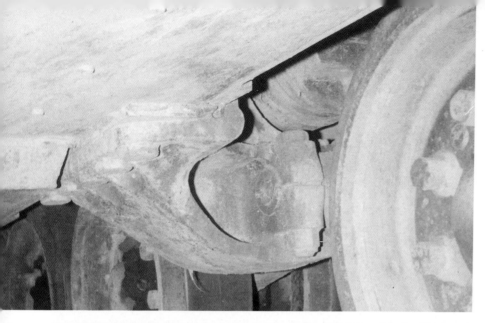

The HVSS unit was bolted to the bottom of the hull and held in place by five bolts. Unlike the VVSS units, the HVSS did not come into contact with the side of the hull. The bracket had a small lip, which formed a 90° angle to provide stability and stop play in the unit while the tank moved. The curve in the bracket arm is quite evident when viewed from the side.

Three of the five bolts were set into indentations on the mounting bracket arm. The triangular piece of metal next to the bracket reinforced the hull bottom.

HVSS Suspension Bogey

The four bogie wheels were identical. This is an inner bogie wheel as seen from beneath the tank. The discoloration of the wheel hub is caused by grease, which has leaked out and seeped through the mud and dirt on the hub.

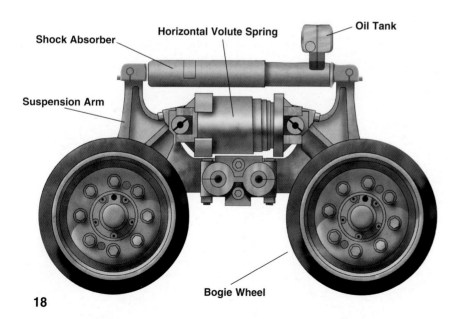

Shock Absorber

Horizontal Volute Spring

Oil Tank

Suspension Arm

Bogie Wheel

18

Drive Sprocket (First Variant)

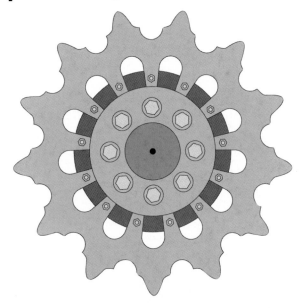

Drive Sprocket (Second Variant)

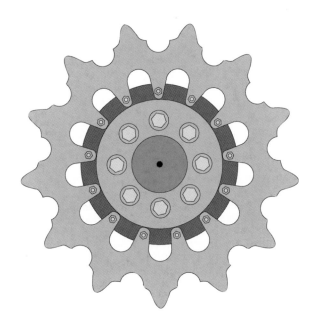

There were three variants of drive sprockets used on the M4. The first actually appeared in three patterns and was identifiable by the round open cutouts. This sprocket was the first version and had two types of dimples on the sprocket face — one triangular and the other oval shaped.

The second variant also had cutouts, but featured a pointed dimple at its tip giving it a distinct angular appearance. Similar patterns were used on both VVSS and HVSS equipped tanks.

(Above) The sprockets were mounted next to the hull with minimal clearance. Both sets of sprocket teeth could be removed from the center wheel drum.

(Above Left) The last variant featured a flat sprocket plate without dimples or cutouts. This unit was particularly common on Shermans during the later years of World War Two and beyond. It was found on both VVSS and HVSS equipped tanks as well as self-propelled guns employing the Sherman chassis.

(Left) There was a modification, which used spacers on the bogies and modified drive sprocket and idler wheel mounts to move the suspension outward. This modification allowed the use of duck-billed end connectors (not shown) on both the inside and outside edges of the track. The effect was to increase track width and decrease ground pressure, thereby improving the Sherman's floatation over soft ground. Tanks so fitted would have added the suffix E9 on their designation, but the introduction of the Easy Eight suspensions with wide tracks made this modification unnecessary. Shermans equipped with standard, i.e. non-spaced, VVSS units often carried the duck-billed end connectors on the outside run of the track during the winter and spring.

Many Shermans were equipped with an open, six-spoked idler wheel. Later vehicles used a six-spoke stamped wheel — a design which emulated that of the later roadwheels. This wheel is fitted with both a grease plug and relief valve. The grease plug is on the lower right of the spoke seen here. Unlike the bogie wheels, rubber tires were not fitted to the idler wheels.

The third idler variant was a twin-wheel unit mounted on M4s equipped with the Horizontal Volute Spring Suspension system. These wheels were equipped with a solid rubber tire bonded to the rim. A grease fitting was incorporated into the dust cap at the middle left. Ten bolts attached the outer wheel to the inner wheel.

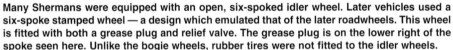

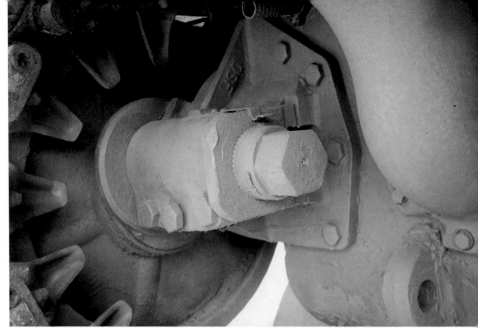

The idler wheel was mounted on an eccentric shaft assembly, which enabled the crew to adjust track tension. The large hex screw in the middle was turned and increased or decreased track tension by moving the wheel forward or backward. Proper tension was essential to keeping the track on the vehicle — especially during combat maneuvers.

The eccentric shaft assembly was similar to that used with the VVSS idler, although there were minor differences in the mounting bracket and some fittings on the housing. The HVSS idler wheel's method of adjusting track tension was identical to that of the VVSS units.

(Above Left) The M4 used a number of different track designs. The first design was the T51, which was similar to the earlier T41 track used on the M3 Lee/Grant. T51 track was prone to slipping on wet or icy surfaces. A variation of this track had two squares cut out of the pad at the top and bottom, giving the pad the appearance of a double 'I' laid end to end. This track, known as WE210 Double I track, was designed in Britain and more commonly seen on British Commonwealth Shermans.

(Above Center) The T48 track was the most common type of rubber block track used on the Sherman. T48 track featured a wide, raised chevron, which provided improved traction in addition to being quieter. Extensive use could wear down the chevron so that it looked like the T51 pad.

(Above Right) T49 steel tracks began being manufactured in 1942 to alleviate the shortage of natural rubber. These tracks featured two sets of parallel bars, or cleats, across the tread. T49 tracks were somewhat uncommon on US M4s, but were widely used on British Commonwealth Shermans.

(Left) The steel T54 track continued the basic design of the rubber T48 track, using a raised chevron to provide increased traction. These tracks were fairly common. This is the T54E1 track.

A slight variation was the T54E2, which had a narrower raised chevron. There were other patterns, but these were the most common. Later composite rubber/steel tracks were also made, but these only saw limited use before the war ended. This vehicle is also equipped with the later drive sprocket and stamped, non-spoked wheels.

T66 Steel Track (WW II)

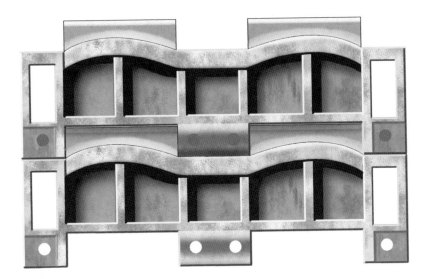

The Horizontal Volute Spring Suspension system introduced a new track design designated the T66. This track was replaced by the T80 track (above), which featured a steel track shoe with a bonded rubber inner pad. T80 track saw some service during WW II, but was more common on post-war M4 tanks. These T80 tracks are fitted to an M40 self-propelled gun which used the lower hull and drive train of the Sherman.

The T84 was the last track used on the HVSS. This track was similar to the late/post war T80, but had a much wider chevron for improved grip on soft surfaces. T84 track was common on post war Shermans as well as the M40/M43 self-propelled guns. In addition to being quieter, rubber shod tracks were easier on the roads of post-war Europe.

The original M4 bogie wheels were identical to those used on the M3's Vertical Volute Spring Suspension (VVSS) system. These wheels had five open spokes and a solid rubber tire bonded to the rim.

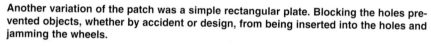

Another variation of the patch was a simple rectangular plate. Blocking the holes prevented objects, whether by accident or design, from being inserted into the holes and jamming the wheels.

The second version was basically the first type with the spokes covered by thin steel plates spot-welded into place. Some of these plates were fairly close to the shape of the spoke holes.

The inner face of the spokes was identical to the outer face. The welded patch is visible through the spoke hole in the lower left of the wheel.

Spoked Wheel Variation (Rare)

A third type of bogie wheel featured a stamped pattern of slightly raised spokes. The top plug near the center is a grease fitting, while the lower plug is a relief valve. This wheel was in common use throughout the latter half of the war.

The final type of bogie wheel used with the VVSS suspension was a simple, smooth dish type, which also featured the grease fitting and relief valve. M4s using a mix of different wheels was a common sight.

Bogie wheels used on the Horizontal Volute Spring Suspension (HVSS) system were totally different from those used on the earlier VVSS units. Twin wheels were attached to each other through a single unit. The large hex screws are bolted to the axle shaft with a dust cap cover and a grease plug located in the center of the ring of hex screws.

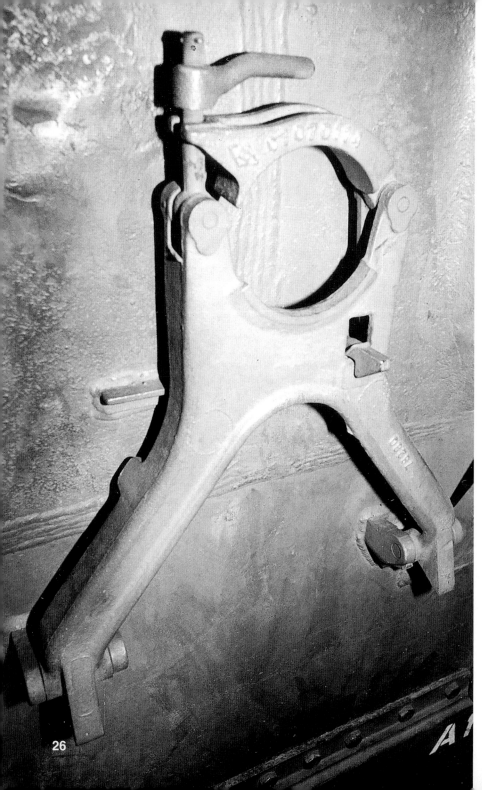

(Above) Most M4s were equipped with a gun travel lock on the glacis plate. The travel lock prevented the gun from moving thereby reducing the strain on the weapon's raising and lowering mechanism. There were at least two different styles of travel lock.

(Left) The travel locks' design and concept were similar, although they differed in the details — leg length, leg width, and latch arrangement.

(Below) Travel locks were used on both the cast and welded hull Shermans without need for modification. This lock uses a single retaining arm and latch to hold the barrel. A second type used a twin clamp.

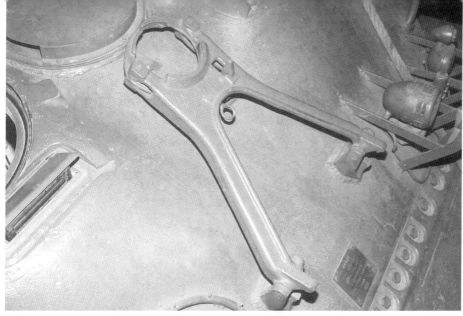

(Above) The travel lock was basically a two legged, triangular unit with a round holder for the barrel at the top. The small protrusion just below the lower lip of the holder is the latch, which holds the unit against the hull when not in use.

(Right) The travel lock was free-swinging when its retaining latch was released. The lock was hand-raised into position. Once raised, the latch was opened and the gun was lowered into position. There were minor differences between the front and back of the travel lock. The barrel grip was spring operated on this version.

(Below) The retaining latch was a simple spring mechanism, which secured the travel lock against the hull when not in use. The pivoting latch slipped through a square slot in the travel lock, which slipped into the small slot on the right of the triangular head.

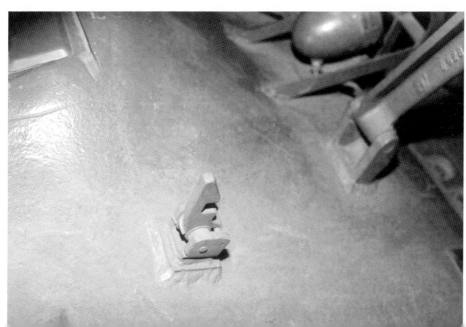

27

Tow cables were carried on the hull for emergencies. A latch held the cable head to the front of the transmission housing.

The latch was a simple hinged arrangement, which was held in place by a butterfly screw. Although the cables could become dirty and slightly oxidized, a thin coating of oil usually kept the cables from rusting outright.

The cable was laid across the hull and held in place by small brackets. Tow cables were made of heavy gauge strands of wire twisted together into a single bundle. These bundles were then twisted together to form the cable.

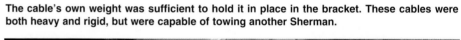

The cable's own weight was sufficient to hold it in place in the bracket. These cables were both heavy and rigid, but were capable of towing another Sherman.

The cable was secured at the hull rear by another latch that was generally similar to the latch mounted at the front. Most Shermans carried at least one cable, although there were some that carried two.

There were two types of hatches for the driver and assistant driver. This early style hatch was narrow, ran parallel to the hull side, and opened to the side. Both hatches were equipped with periscopes.

These hatches were undersized and difficult to get through for all but the smallest individual under the best of conditions. In combat gear and an emergency, the chances for a tanker to get out were extremely slim. The two sets of clips on either side of the front of the hatch are for the foul weather hood and windscreen.

The hatches were counterbalanced using a coiled steel spring. The spring lessened the effort required to open and close the hatch. Nevertheless, this hatch was still a detriment to a quick escape.

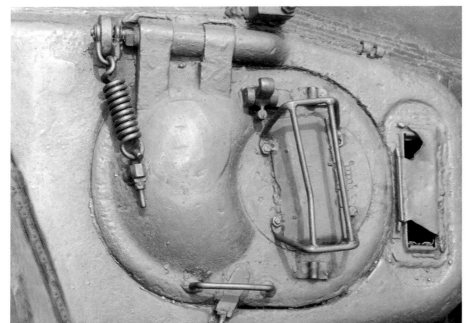

29

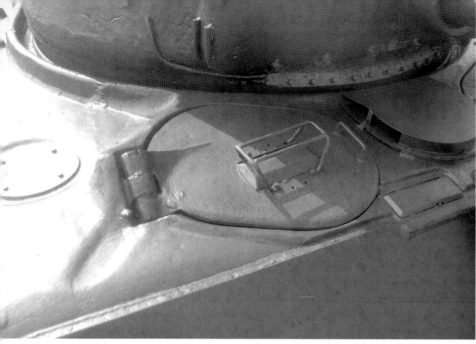

In an attempt to improve the crew access and emergency escape situation, a new, larger hatch was designed. These were angled to the hull and the hinge was located at the rounded corner rather than on the side. These hatches were counterbalanced internally.

The hatch opened out to the side and forward to clear the turret. Both styles of hatches had a periscope, which revolved for all-round vision. The M6 periscope was composed of two prisms in a metal shell. Both hatches were fitted with a handle for pulling the hatch closed.

The new hatch was a definite improvement and made entry and exit much easier. The new hatches were turned at a 45° angle to the hull side. A rubber seal around the edge of the hatch opening kept water from dripping into the hull.

In the event of damage, the periscope could be easily replaced by pressing the button in the center and sliding it out of the mount. Spares were carried within the hull. The M6 was subject to interior condensation and, late in the war, a new solid plastic block with reflective surfaces was developed under the designation M13.

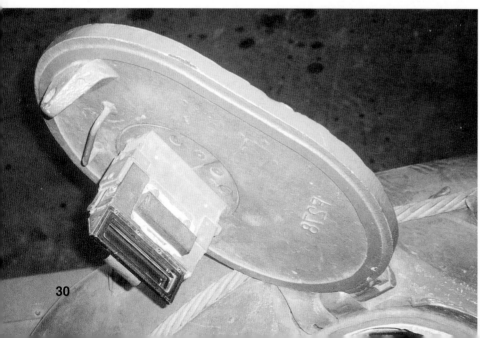

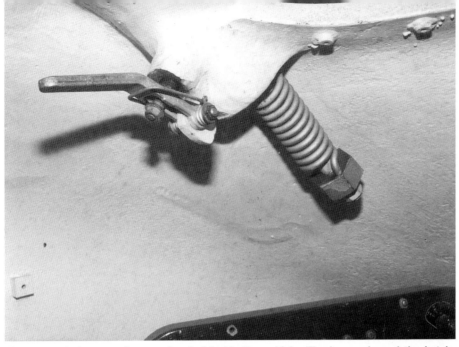

The counterbalance spring was located inside the vehicle. The lever released the hatch, which easily sprang open. The hull and turret interiors were painted white to improve lighting, however, the inner face of the hatch was painted Olive Drab.

A side opening panel with a spring latch allowed access to the medical kit. The medical kit was the standard type for use in the field and was carried on or in most vehicles for emergency use on the battlefield.

A late modification was the addition of a small first aid kit to the side of the hull. The first aid kit was normally welded to the center of the left side of the hull, although other locations were not unusual.

The kit carried a variety of bandages, ointments, and antiseptics for treating wounds and injuries until a qualified medic could reach the scene or the injured soldier could be taken to an aid station. First aid was — and is — a regular part of a soldier's training.

31

Early Shermans had direct vision ports for the drivers incorporated into the armored hoods. These ports were considered a weak point in the armor and were soon deleted. The splash ring in front of the vision port deflected machine gun rounds away from the port.

The pop-up periscope in the roof of the drivers' hoods was retained. This assistant driver's periscope is in the extended position. The cover was spring loaded and came down when the periscope was retracted. This periscope was fixed facing forward. An additional periscope was mounted in the hatch and could be rotated to view out to the side of the vehicle.

A sheet metal cover was mounted over the ventilator blower on the M4A1. The screen over the vent is barely visible under the open side toward the side and rear. The hull and turret ventilators were designed to pull in fresh air and prevent gun, fuel, and oil fumes from building up within the vehicle.

The M4A3 was equipped with two hull ventilators. These ventilators were positioned on either side of the drivers' positions. A raised armored splash ring protected the ventilators. Prominent manufacturer's casting numbers are visible on top the ventilator cover. Two drain holes, visible at lower left, prevented water from collecting in the ventilator housing.

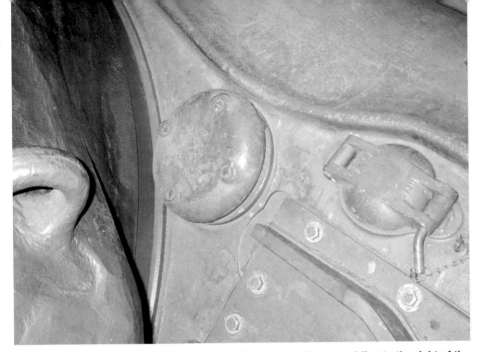

The rear ventilator was just in front of the right fuel tank. The curved line to the right of the ventilator and fuel cap is a bullet splash rail. Splash rails, in one form or another, were located in several places around the hull. These were designed to deflect small arms and machine gun fire from damaging ancillary components on the hull. Other splash rails were designed to deflect fire away from openings such as view slits and machine gun ports.

M4A3s featured a different fuel cap arrangement. The auxiliary fuel cap is to the left, while the closest two caps in the center are for the main fuel tanks. The cap in the center is the oil fill port, while the furthest cap fills another main fuel tank. Although the locations varied, the general design of the fuel caps and the method of operation was generally identical.

A fire extinguisher handle, its cover, and the auxiliary fuel tank filler port were located on the left side just behind the turret. Fire extinguisher nozzles were arranged around the interior of the engine compartment. The extinguishers could be activated both internally (by the driver) and externally.

An 'L' shaped pin held the armored fuel tank cap in place. Removing the pin allowed the cap to pivot upward. The fuel cap was opened by lifting the 'C' shaped ring and twisting it counter-clock-wise. Depending on the version, the number of gasoline fuel caps on the M4A1 and M4A3 varied from two to four, the early models initially having four, with the later vehicles deleting the inner caps.

Equipment was stored on the rear sides of the hull and on the rear deck on some models. The empty rack for the shovel is at the top right on this M4A3. The axe holder is next to the lifting ring, while the pick holder is located forward.

The track tension bar was mounted on the left side. Some M4A3s were also equipped with brackets for the idler wrench and sledge hammer. Many of these brackets were simple pieces of sheet metal bent to shape and welded to the hull.

This restored vehicle has each piece of equipment neatly labeled, but under combat conditions these labels would be quickly worn away or painted over. An embossed plate labeled 'GASOLINE' at left warns the crew to fill the tank with fuel versus oil. This is the standard arrangement of equipment on the right rear side of the M4A1, although there were some variations — especially after the vehicle was issued to a crew.

M4A1s had their sledge hammer and idler tension wrench stored behind the engine door cover. On the M4A3, these would have been stored in a similar fashion, but with more distance in between them due to the larger hatch size. At the top of the photo is the folding luggage rack, which began coming into service in 1944.

The shovel is on the left side of this M4A1 versus the right side of an M4A3. Additional tie down loops, spot welded to the hull, are used to hold down tarps and additional equipment. The shovel tie down is faintly visible by the bottom of the leather strap holding the shovel in place.

The underside of the luggage rack had gun barrel cleaning rod holders, while straps were placed on top to hold equipment in place. In addition to vehicle and pioneer tools, Shermans were usually covered with additional stowage ranging from camouflage nets to the crews' personal kits. The external phone box is located at right.

The rack was raised to allow access to the rear engine compartment doors. The brush is for cleaning out the main gun barrel. The rods were screwed together to form a single, long pole. The holder is latched and swings open to allow access to the equipment.

The holder on the other side is fixed and serves as the anchor point for the rods. The wooden cleaning rods could be left in a natural wood color, but were more often simply painted Olive Drab — the same color used on the tank.

The external phone box, mounted on the right rear corner of the hull, allowed infantrymen to direct the tank while it was buttoned up. Pulling the long U-shaped handle on the right opened the box.

The phone box was secured to the hull rear by brackets on either side of the box. The box provided protection form the elements and some protection from shrapnel, but was otherwise vulnerable to heavier small arms and machine gun fire.

The phone handset was similar to the standard Signal Corps type used with radios. The coiled wire allowed the caller to stand away from the vehicle's engine noise and better observe the surroundings. The knob on the small box in the upper left corner was a volume control. A schematic pattern is located on the inside of the cover.

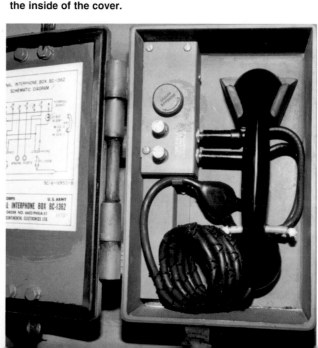

Not all Shermans were fitted with the external phone box. Many M4s had spare track block holders placed on either side of the hull rear. Each holder held three track pads. The metal strips on either side were hinged to release the pads.

The Sherman's tail lights were identical on both the welded and cast hull M4s, however the brush guards were slightly different due to the hull shape. On the cast hull the guards were larger and more angular in appearance. There was also a small bulge on the hull for the mounting point.

Tail lights on welded hull M4A3s were identical, but lacked the small spacer between the light and the hull. The brush guard was also smaller and more rounded. Comparing the mounting bracket to the cast hull shows how this light almost makes contact with the top of the deck and the lack of an extension on the bottom of the unit where it meets the hull. The height of the light on the cast hull was much higher than this unit.

The bulge for the taillight mount was cast into the hull. The electrical wire ran inside the bracket and through the spacer between the light and hull. An intake, protected with a wire mesh screen, is immediately adjacent to the light.

M4A3E8 (76) W HVSS Sherman

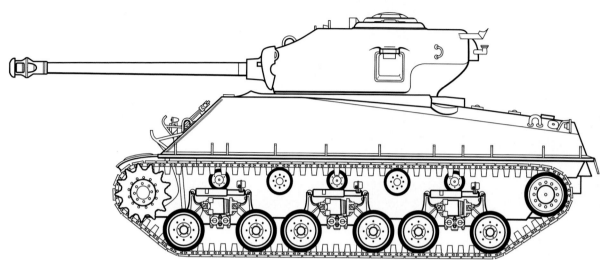

Specifications

Length: 24.75 Feet (7.54 м)
Width: 9.83 Feet (3 м)
Height: 9.75 Feet (2.97 м)
Weight (Empty): 68,100 lbs (30,890 кg)
Weight (Loaded): 74,200 lbs (33,657 кg)
Powerplant: Ford GAA V-8, 500 hp
Transmission: Syncromesh, 5 speeds Forward, 1 Reverse
Speed: 26 mph (41.8 кмн)
Range: 100 miles (161 км)
Armament: 1 x 76mm Gun, 1 x .50 Caliber MG, 2 x .30 Caliber MG
Crew: 5

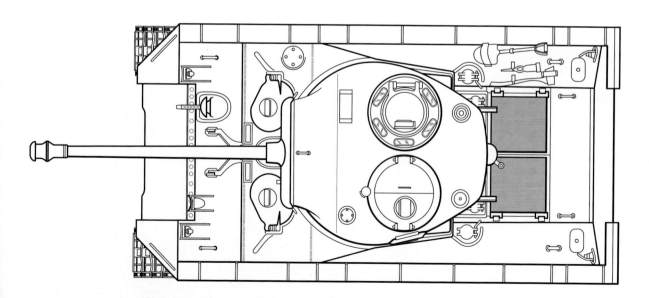

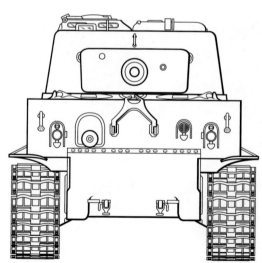

The cast turret had a rough exterior finish. From left to right are the commander's vane sight, a periscope cover, lift ring, ventilator dome, and periscope cover (which lacks the wire guard). This turret — from a 75 ᴍᴍ gun armed M4A3 — has been retrofitted with a late style commander's cupola. Some Sherman turrets, most notably those equipped with the 75 ᴍᴍ gun, were equipped with a smoke grenade mortar firing through a port in the turret roof. The welded over port is visible at lower right.

The spotlight screw is located at the junction of the 'L' shaped bracket. The cap attached to the chain covers the opening when the searchlight was stowed. The holes at the base of the ventilator prevented water from pooling in the housing.

Most Shermans were equipped with a small spotlight — normally mounted in front of the ventilator. The spotlight could be aimed vertically by tightening or loosening a screw on the back of the handle. The spotlight could also be hand held and was stored inside the turret rear when not in use.

Two antenna mounts were built into the rear of the turret. Most tanks were not fitted with a second radio; consequently this mount was covered with a plate.

39

Spare tracks could be mounted on the turret side. With the tracks and brackets removed the attachment points were visible. These were simple rods with a screw fitting welded to the side of the turret. Tracks could be mounted on one or both sides of the turret.

The tracks were held in place by half 'C' shaped brackets, each held in place by a screw. In sufficient quantities, the pads also doubled as additional armor protection. The mounting points also served to hold additional crew equipment. Additional track pads were also mounted on the corners of the rear hull plate.

Lift rings were welded to both sides of the turret. These rings allowed a crane to lift the turret off the hull and provide ready access to the hull interior. Such operations were usually confined to heavy maintenance units behind the front lines.

An armored cover protected the gunner's periscope on the T23 turret. The gunner used an M4A1 periscope, which could also be used to lay the gun on a target. To the right of the cover is the base of the tank commander's vane sight.

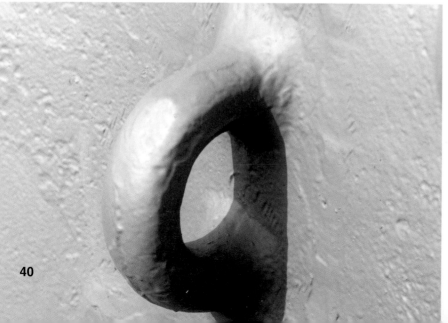

The device next to the commander's cupola is the folding .50 caliber gun barrel clamp. When not in use, the clamp was folded down. A locking mechanism held it in either position. The numbers cast into the turret at left served to identify the turret manufacturer and lot number. The number location and style varied from one manufacturer to another.

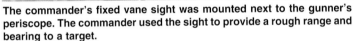

The commander's fixed vane sight was mounted next to the gunner's periscope. The commander used the sight to provide a rough range and bearing to a target.

The loader used an M6 periscope until it was replaced with one less prone to the effects of humidity and dampness. Most periscopes were protected by a heavy wire brush guard bolted to the periscope housing.

Periscopes were also protected by a spring loaded cover, which popped open when the periscope was raised into position. The wire guard was sufficiently strong to protect the periscope from crewmen's feet. Both the cover and brush guard were mounted on the rotating periscope housing.

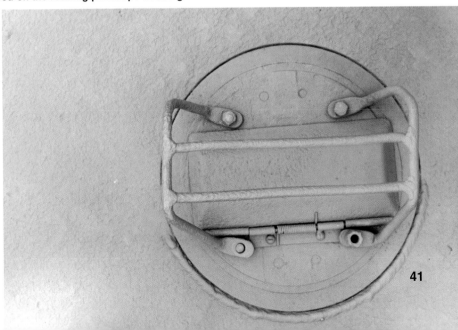

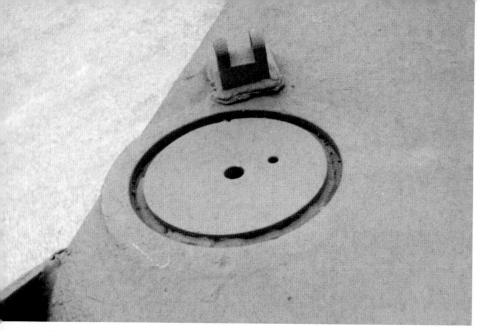

The T23 turret — used on the 76 MM gun equipped Shermans — was usually equipped with two antenna mounts. The mounts were placed on top of the turret bustle where they had a direct line to the radios mounted inside the turret rear.

The T23 turret was both larger and less rounded than the 75 MM gun turrets. The upper edge was nearly squared off, while the sides had a slight slope.

The rear of the T23 turret sloped upward at a pronounced angle, but was flat at the top — a reverse of the smaller 75 MM turret design. Both turret designs featured rear mounted lift rings. The protruding bar at the top right is the bracket for storing the .50 caliber machine gun.

The T23 turret also had a rough cast appearance. A prominent weld seam indicates where the top and bottom sections of the turret were joined together. Lifting rings were welded to the sides of the turret bustle.

A third lift ring was welded to the front center of the turret roof, just behind the gun mount. Square plates, used for mounting the foul weather cover, were welded around the periphery of the gun mount. Numbers cast into the turret served to identify the turret model and manufacturer — their location varied.

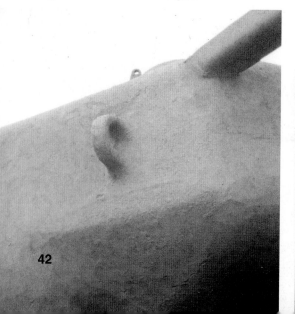

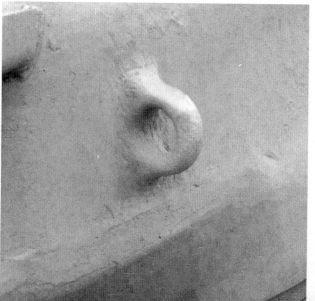

The original gun mount, equipped with a narrow mantlet, was designated M34. The co-axial machine gun is just visible beneath the 75 MM gun barrel. The mantlet — or rotor shield — was barely wider than the gun barrel. The M34 lacked a direct telescopic sight. The 75 MM gun's sighting was accomplished using a periscope.

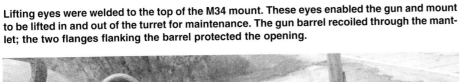

Lifting eyes were welded to the top of the M34 mount. These eyes enabled the gun and mount to be lifted in and out of the turret for maintenance. The gun barrel recoiled through the mantlet; the two flanges flanking the barrel protected the opening.

The co-axial .30 caliber machine gun fired through a separate slot to the left of the main gun. The machine gun was normally protected by a separate armored block mounted over the gun barrel.

The M34 gun mount was held in place by twenty-five bolts screwed into the turret facing and held in place with nuts on the inside.

43

A number of early M34 mounts were modified for telescopic sights. The mantlet had an extension welded on the right side to cover the sight. The weld beads on this mantlet run vertically.

On this mantlet the weld beads run horizontally, indicating it was from a batch by a different manufacturer. The modified M34 mantlets still lacked an extension over the co-axial machine gun. The machine gun retained the separate armored block used on the earlier mantlets.

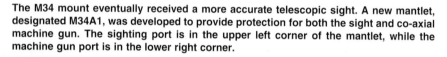

The M34 mount eventually received a more accurate telescopic sight. A new mantlet, designated M34A1, was developed to provide protection for both the sight and co-axial machine gun. The sighting port is in the upper left corner of the mantlet, while the machine gun port is in the lower right corner.

The new mantlet was curved to conform to the face of the gun mount set into the front of the turret. The extended left side of the shield deleted the need for a separate shield over the coaxial machine gun.

The introduction of the T23 turret and its 76 MM gun required a new gun mount designated T62. The shield was symmetrical, except for the position of the sighting and machine gun ports. The bars welded on the sides are a post-war modification for attaching a canvas cover.

The new gun shield was 3.5 inches (8.9 CM) thick. Lift rings, located on the upper corners of the shield, allowed the weapon to be removed from the turret.

The lift rings angled outward from the shield at about 45˚. The shield was attached to the gun mount, which was held in place by a trunnion pin attached to the flanges on the turret front.

Later model T23 turrets had a modified shield, which lacked the lift rings. The front of the gun mount is barely visible in the gap between the shield and the front of the turret.

45

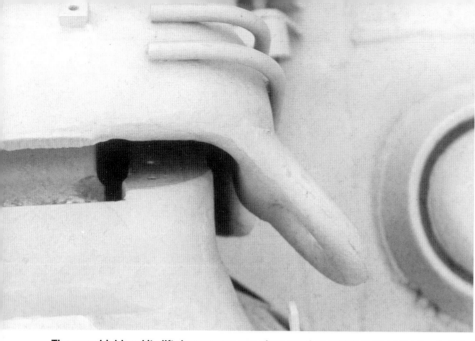

The gun shield and its lift rings were a one piece casting, which cupped the front of the turret. The gun was raised and lowered on a heavy trunnion pin. Removing the pin allowed the entire shield, gun, and mount to be removed for maintenance.

The canvas cover was held in place by metal 'L' brackets screwed down against the lip of the canvas cover. A second piece of canvas covered the lift ring weld on the turret roof.

Late production T23 shields lacked the side lifting rings and were usually fitted with a canvas dust and foul weather cover. Canvas covers were sometimes painted to match the rest of the vehicle.

These 'L' shaped brackets were on both the turret and shield and provided a substantial anchor point for the canvas cover when properly screwed down.

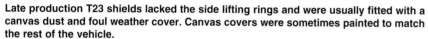

The development of a 105 MM howitzer armed M4 resulted in a new, more rounded mantlet. The vehicle was developed to provide armored battalions with additional fire support. The new M52 gun mount was easily recognized due to its rounded silhouette. The M52 mantlet was similar to the M34A1, but covered the entire front of the gun mount and lacked the cutout on the side. The gunner's sight is on the left, just below the lift ring.

Additional canvas attachment points were mounted to the turret face. Grommets on the canvas cover snapped onto the small pins. The mantlet was 3.6 inches (9.14 CM) thick and had two lift rings on top of it. The rough cast texture of the turret and the lift rings is very evident. Attachment points for a canvas cover follow the outline of the rear of the mantlet.

The M4 (105 MM) mount was also equipped with a co-axial .30 caliber machine gun. The howitzer was mounted in both the M4 and M4A3 models of the Sherman. The studded tube surrounding the shield served as a mounting point for a foul weather cover.

A small collar surrounds both the gunner's sighting port and the co-axial machine gun port. The collar strengthens the area around the hole and serves as a rain gutter. Circular lifting rings were welded to the top of the shield.

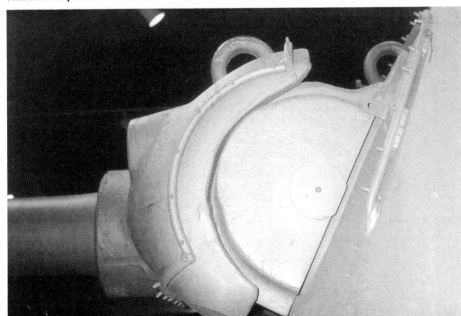

A new version of the Sherman, designated M4A3E2, was developed in 1944 to serve as an assault tank. Known as the 'Jumbo', the vehicle featured a new turret, which superficially resembled the T23 albeit with much thicker armor — six inches (15.24 CM) — on the sides and rear. The shell ejection port on the left side was eliminated.

The front shield was seven inches (17.8 CM) thick. This was achieved by welding a slab of armor to the M62 gun mount. The top of the turret was one inch (2.54 CM) thick and was welded to the shell of the turret. The weld seam is visible just behind the lift ring.

Originally it had been intended to arm the 'Jumbo' with the 76 MM gun, but since it was decided that the Jumbo was going to be used against fortifications, the 75 MM gun would be a better choice for this role. Later some 'Jumbo's' were rearmed with the 76 MM gun for use against German tanks.

This M4A3E2 under restoration at the Jacques Littlefield Collection gives a unique view of the added armor thickness of the front hull. In addition to this added armor, a thicker differential/final drive housing was cast with a thickness up to 5.5 inches (14 CM). The additional armor increased the Jumbo's overall weight to some 42 tons (38.1 MT), necessitating the use of duckbill extenders and a reduction in the final drive ratio.

M4's used two basic types of commander's hatches on their turrets. The first hatch was a simple split unit, which featured a single periscope incorporated into one of the hatches. The periscope was located in a swivel mount which provided a 360˚ field of view when the tank was buttoned up.

An anti-aircraft machine gun mount was attached to the rotating hatch ring. The hatch ring rotated on ball bearings. This arrangement allowed the commander's machine gun to be turned in any direction and still afford some measure of protection for the commander.

Clips were mounted on each side of the hatch ring to hold the split hatches in the open position. The two hatches were heavy and not counter-balanced; consequently the two hatches were difficult to open.

When the machine gun was stowed, the two hatches could still clear the barrel although it was a close fit. The barrel bracket could be swung down to the side when not in use. The commander used a standard M6 periscope.

The gun barrel stowage bracket was hinged to fold down. A small lever helped to keep the bracket in either the raised or stowed position.

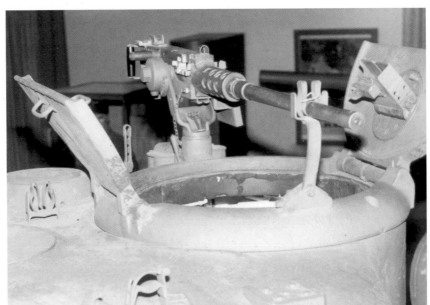

49

The early split hatch was replaced by a new cupola equipped with six vision ports and a single piece hatch. The new cupola improved both access to the turret and vision. A rotating M6 periscope was mounted in the hatch.

Despite the slightly smaller diameter of the new hatch, there was still ample room for entry and exit. Emergency exit was greatly helped by the commander having to only open a single hatch, versus the two hatches in the earlier cupola. A rubber gasket sealed the opening against water entry.

Ball bearings allowed the center of the hatch to rotate through 360°. This capability provided the commander with a full periscopic view around the tank when the hatch was closed.

The commander's periscope was identical to those used by both the driver and assistant driver. The black object in the center of the periscope is a pad to protect the commander's forehead.

The hatch was hinged around a single bolt. The latch at right locked the hatch in the open position.

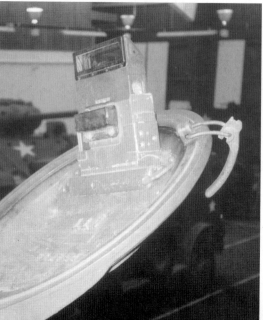

Early M4s were equipped with a single turret hatch making emergency escape for the turret crew difficult at best. Later Shermans were equipped with a second hatch in the turret roof. Initially, this loader's hatch was the old split type used by the commander. Later, a less complicated — and lighter — oval hatch was designed as a replacement.

The hatch featured a large pad to protect the loader's head. Nevertheless, helmets — tanker's or combat — were required. The lever rotated parallel to the hatch to secure it against the inside of the turret roof.

The addition of this second hatch reduced crew losses in combat, since escape was now much easier through the large opening. Counter-balancing springs on the hatch made it fairly easy to open.

The fully opened hatch was held in place by a small retaining latch. The hatch fit into the small notch at left. The spring loaded latch was simply pushed back to release the hatch.

Most Shermans featured a shell ejection port on the left side of the turret. The crew used the hatch to discard used expended shell casings or bring in fresh air and vent the turret. The hatch was too small to be used as an escape hatch.

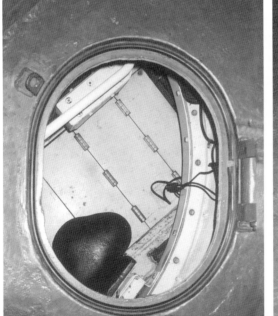

The crew used a lever attached to the flap to push it out and up. The flap interior, like the crew hatches, was painted the exterior color. A rubber seal around the inside of the hatch kept out rain water.

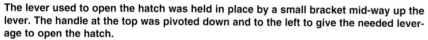

The lever used to open the hatch was held in place by a small bracket mid-way up the lever. The handle at the top was pivoted down and to the left to give the needed leverage to open the hatch.

The hatch was hinged at the top and fitted into a molded recess in the turret side. Slots on the sides allowed the hinge pin to be removed.

M4s were originally equipped with a .50 caliber anti-aircraft machine gun, but this was quickly changed to a lighter .30 caliber weapon in September of 1942. Reports from North Africa resulted in the .50 caliber MG again becoming standard by the following February. This .50 caliber machine gun is fitted on the early split type commander's hatch. The ammunition was normally fed from the left side of the weapon. Spent casings and links were ejected out the right side. This weapon has been fitted with the less common square ammunition container.

This .50 caliber machine gun is fitted with the more common standard ammunition box and support tray. The box and tray clipped onto the machine gun mount. The ammunition box held 105 rounds of linked .50 caliber ammunition. The slotted cooling jacket on the machine gun barrel was more common on post-war vehicles.

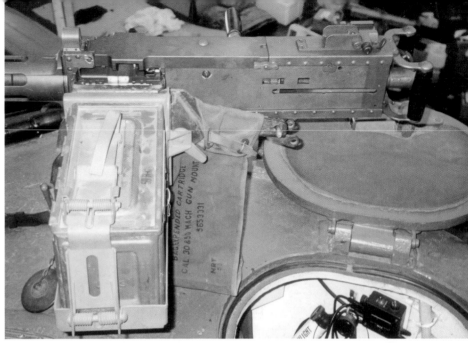

The ammunition can was held in the tray by a spring-loaded clamp. The box held 105 rounds of armor piercing, incendiary, and tracer ammunition. Designed for anti-aircraft defense, the .50 caliber MG was just as effective against ground troops and soft-skin vehicles.

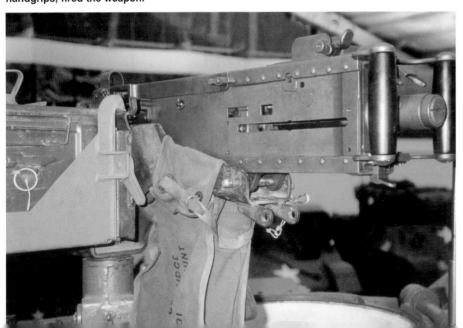

A canvas bag was mounted beneath the machine gun to catch spent shell casings. These bags were not always fitted. A thumb operated butterfly switch, barely visible between the handgrips, fired the weapon.

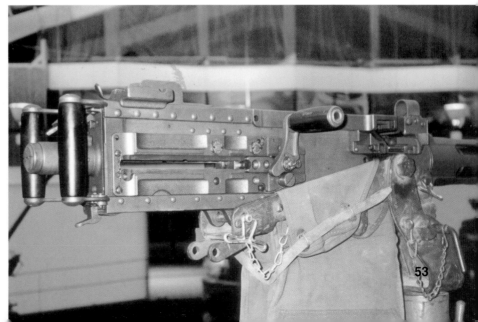

The right side of the machine gun was similar to the left except for the cocking handle. Pulling the handle down and back cocked the weapon.

The pintle was bolted to a mounting plate welded to the turret top. Removing the four bolts allowed the post to be folded over. The handle attached to the post is a locking lever to hold the machine gun in place.

The mounting plate for the MG pintle was a simple flat plate welded to the turret roof.

The hinge for the folding pintle mount is at the bottom right side of the mount. M4s equipped with the split type commander's hatch lacked this mount. Split commander's hatches used a post attached directly to the outer hatch ring.

M4s equipped with the 105 MM howitzer were fitted with an extra ventilator at the rear of the turret. The new ventilator housing required a redesigned machine gun mount. The slotted housing allowed the blower to do its job and still provide a strong mounting for the machine gun.

The entire machine gun assembly fitted into the pintle post, which was bolted onto the top of the turret. When the machine gun was not mounted a small cap — chained to the pintle — was placed over the top to keep out moisture.

The machine gun could be broken down and stored across the turret bustle when not in use. The gun cradle was locked into the middle socket, while the cooling jacket was clipped into the frame at left. The gun barrel was clipped into the arms welded to the corners of the bustle. A circular cup protecting an antenna mount was cast into the left rear corner of the turret bustle. A second antenna mount was welded to the bustle top, just to the right of the centerline.

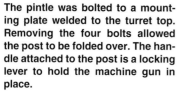

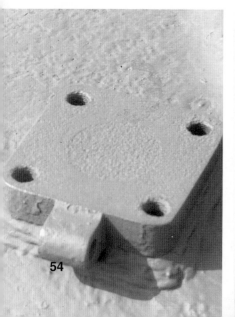

A storage mount for the machine gun was welded to the rear of the turret. The lever kept the mount from being jarred out when the tank was on the move.

The socket and locking lever allowed the weapon to be removed from the stowage mount in a manner of seconds.

The bracket for holding the cooling jacket was open to allow the gun barrel to pass through it. The spring kept pressure on the barrel to hold it in place.

(Below Center and Right) 'L' brackets welded to the rear corners of the bustle were equipped with clamps to hold the barrel in place when it was removed from the receiver. The barrel was forced down into the groove in the center of the bracket.

T23 turrets employed a slightly different machine gun stowage arrangement. The storage mount was attached to the blower vent cover and angled to the left side. The modified cooling jacket clamp was now attached to the left barrel holding bracket.

Battle experience indicated some weak points in the Sherman's armor, particularly over the ammunition storage areas. One-inch thick slabs of armor plate were welded over the two ammunition positions on the right side of the hull to improve their protection.

The weld seam on the front armor plate slightly overlapped the hull weld seam. The hull and armor plate weld seams had a slightly different look. The welds were normally beveled, since squared edges could be an effective shot trap.

A single armor plate was welded over the port ammunition storage bin. The later development of 'wet storage' ammunition bins inside the hull helped to lessen the problem of ammunition fires. Nevertheless, armor protection was never the Sherman's strong suit.

The application of external armor plate took more effort on some tanks due to the contour of the hull resulting in some interesting weld patterns. Plates attached in the field had a much rougher look than those added on the assembly line.

External armor plate welded over the assistant driver's compartment required a small cutout to clear the hull machine gun position. The weld seam at the top gives a good idea of how much work was involved in installing these plates.

Additional armor was also welded in front of the drivers' positions. A solid plate was welded at the top and bottom of the protruding drivers' compartments. Effective against handheld anti-tank weapons and glancing hits from some of the larger German tanks guns, the add on armor was still no match for the larger 75 MM and 88 MM guns used by the German Panther and Tiger.

Additional armor plates were welded over the front right side of the turret which had been thinned down on the inside to accommodate the gun controls. This design flaw was rectified on later turrets, but this plate still helped to improve the protection on this part of the turret.

This M4A1 interior shows a fully-equipped tank. Spare periscopes, a foul weather hood, and a .45 caliber M3 'grease gun' are mounted above or on the transmission housing.

This M4 has had its interior gutted except for the drive train, which allows a good overall view of the transmission housing. The small open tube on the right is the differential breather.

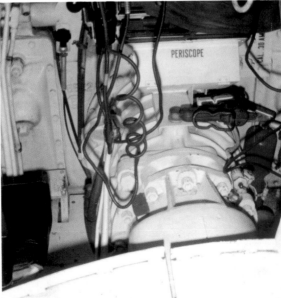

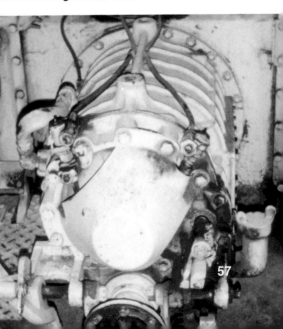

57

The driver controlled the tank using two steering levers, which braked the tracks. The driver's instrument panel was set into the left sponson and angled about 45° to the driver. The clutch pedal is to the left of the steering levers, while the accelerator pedal is to the right.

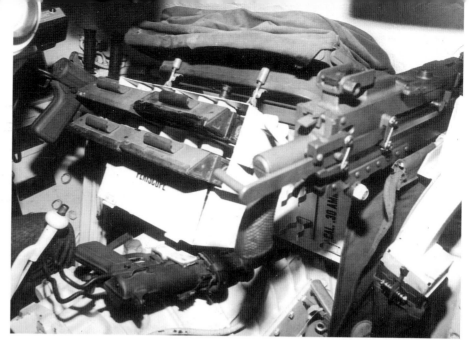

The assistant driver's .45 caliber M3 submachine gun was mounted on top of transmission housing to prevent it from interfering with operation of the hull .30 caliber machine gun. The M3 used the same ammunition as the Thompson sub-machine gun.

Four periscopes were carried above the transmission housing. The driver's M3 was mounted in the left side of the periscope box. The black cord hanging down is for the crew's interphone system.

Both the driver's and assistant driver's M3s were secured by leather straps. Both weapons were placed in a metal clip and secured with a leather strap. Canvas webbing, riveted onto the clip, served as a chaffing pad.

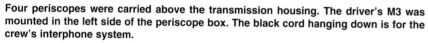

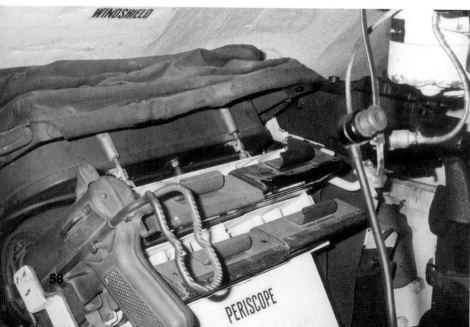

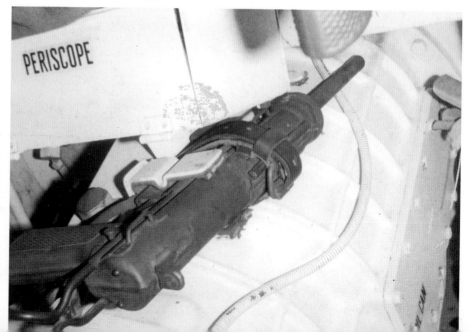

58

The driver's instrument panel was relatively simple. The panel was mounted at a 45° angle to the driver. Panel and main light switches, flanking a row of circuit breakers, were mounted across the top. The second row consisted of ammeter, oil pressure, water temperature, and fuel gauges. Below these were the large speedometer and tachometer. The 60 mph (96.5 KMH) speed limit on the speedometer was rather optimistic.

The gearshift lever was attached to the transmission housing directly to the driver's right. Pushing in the clutch pedal and pressing the button on top of the handle released the lever and allowed the driver to select the proper gear. The transmission had five forward speeds and one reverse.

(Above, Right, and Below) The horn control box was mounted on the right steering lever. Cable conduits leading outside to the lights and siren are visible behind the steering levers. The rubber grips of the steering levers stopped just short of the underside of the glacis plate. The maximum speed of the M4A1 was 24 mph (38.6 KMH). Each steering lever was connected via rods to the steering units at the front of the tank. Pulling a lever back braked the track on that side, resulting in the tank turning into the slow track. The Sherman could be steered with driver's head out of the hatch or completely closed up.

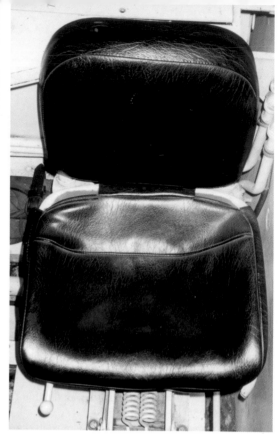

(Above) M4s were equipped with an escape hatch set into the floor behind the assistant driver. Turning the lever clockwise pulled the retaining rods back allowing the hatch to drop to the ground.

(Right) Later model seats were mounted on a spring loaded lever that was adjusted by a handle on the right side. This is the driver's seat and the spring arrangement is visible at the front of the seat.

(Left) The control layout of this early M4A3 was similar to the M4A1's drivers' compartment. One minor difference was the metal ratchet strips at the base of the steering levers.

(Below) Both drivers' seats could be raised to allow them to ride with their heads outside the roof hatches. The seat could be quickly dropped with one hand and the hatch closed with the other when necessary.

(Above) The under hull escape hatch stood proud of the hull's bottom plate. Clearance between the bottom of the hull and the ground was less than 20 inches (50.8 CM).

(Right) The M6 periscope was used by all the crewmembers except the gunner. A later periscope, the M13, was developed late in the war to combat condensation problems. The gunner used an M4 periscope equipped with a telescopic sight.

(Below) The 60˚ glacis plate on the early welded hull M4s required the use of extended driver's boxes over the front of the hull. Early drivers' boxes had a direct vision port, but later vehicles used a periscope set into the box roof. The periscopes were fixed forward, but the periscopes in the hatches could be rotated through 360˚.

M4 hulls were equipped with hull ventilator fans to vent fuel, oil, and gun fumes from the vehicle's interior. This fan is located between the drivers' positions on a late production M4A1. Early M4A1s had a single fan adjacent to the assistant driver, while welded hull M4s had fans flanking both drivers' positions.

The welded hull had a little more space than the cast hull. Additionally, the hull machine gun was set into an outward bulged plate welded into the glacis plate. So many welds across the glacis plate created weak spots in the armor.

The .30 caliber M1919A4 hull machine gun was set into a ball mount and fired by the assistant driver. Originally there were two fixed machine guns next to the ball mount, but these were quickly eliminated from the design. The holder for the ammunition is the white object attached to bolt assembly.

Machine gun ammunition was stored in racks next to the assistant driver's position. Officially, between 4750 and 6250 rounds of .30 caliber ammunition could be carried internally depending on the Sherman variant. Crews in regular contact with the enemy often stowed additional ammunition — both main and machine gun — in any available space within the hull.

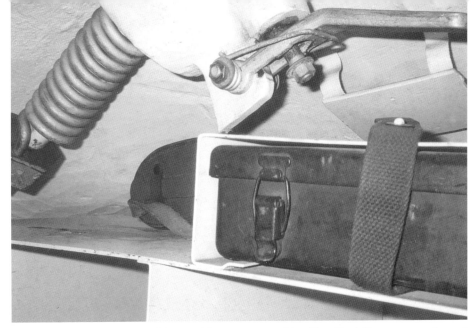

A tool kit was stored on top of the machine gun ammunition bins. Each Sherman was issued with a basic set of mechanic's tools, since routine vehicle maintenance was the crew's responsibility. The lever and spring was part of the assistant driver's hatch mechanism. The spring counterbalanced the weight of the hatch.

Additional bins were located on the driver's side of the Sherman. Spare headlights are stored on the side of the cabinet. The sharp 60° angle of the hull on the early M4A3 can be easily discerned from the side. Later vehicles had a 47° glacis plate that increased the interior space and eliminated the drivers' extension boxes.

An electrical relay box was mounted next to the driver's instrument panel in this M4A1. The Sherman had three sources of 24 volt electrical power: the vehicle batteries (two 12V batteries wired in series), an engine driven generator, and an auxiliary generator.

Internal stowage arrangements varied according to the model of M4. This cast hull M4A1 has spare headlights stowed on top of a bin next to the driver. The round object above the headlight is a small light. The switch for it is located on the edge in the center.

All Shermans were equipped with a gasoline powered auxiliary generator mounted at the rear of the left sponson. The generator's fuel tank is located at the lower right. The primer pump is the long rod sticking up just above the fuel tank. The unit provided electrical power without the need to start the engine.

63

Both the M4 and M4A1 used the Continental R975 C1 engine, which superseded the earlier R975 EC2 used in the first production models. The R975 C1 was a nine-cylinder, air-cooled, four cycle radial engine using 80 octane gasoline. An improved model — the R975 C4 shown here — replaced the C1.

The pipes around the outside of the engine are the exhaust manifold assembly, while the two at the bottom are the intake manifolds leading to the carburetor. The circular fuel pump is mounted just above the two intake manifolds. The two round devices on either side of the square in the middle are the magnetos. The cylindrical starter motor is centered just above the magnetos.

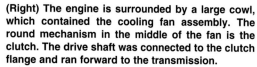

(Left) The engine sat in an oval-shaped, transverse beam, which served as a mounting base within the engine compartment. The wire assembly between the ends of the exhaust manifold is the distributor. The carburetor is located at the bottom between the scoops. The R975 was a derivative of the air-cooled Wright R975 aircraft engine used to power a number of early US Army Air Corps basic trainers. Wright, having to focus their construction efforts on building aircraft engines for both the US Navy and Air Corps, passed the construction of the R975 to Continental.

(Right) The engine is surrounded by a large cowl, which contained the cooling fan assembly. The round mechanism in the middle of the fan is the clutch. The drive shaft was connected to the clutch flange and ran forward to the transmission.

Engine access was provided via these large armored doors, as well as the hatch on the engine deck. The silver pipes connect the air cleaners — located on either side of the access doors — to the intake manifolds. The R975 C4 began to be used in tanks manufactured in 1944. It was also retrofitted in the field to tanks equipped with the R975 C1.

The carburetor was mounted at the lower rear of the engine with the fuel pump mounted just above it. The two magnetos are mounted above and to the left and right of the fuel pump.

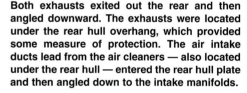

Both exhausts exited out the rear and then angled downward. The exhausts were located under the rear hull overhang, which provided some measure of protection. The air intake ducts lead from the air cleaners — also located under the rear hull — entered the rear hull plate and then angled down to the intake manifolds.

Looking down through the open engine deck reveals the upper arm of the engine mount. The exhaust pipes run over the top of the engine and exit at the rear under the hull overhang.

The air breather, between the bends in the exhaust pipes, the starter, and the magnetos could be reached through the upper deck hatch.

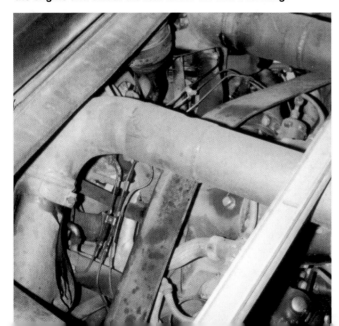

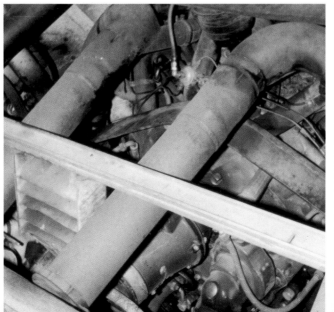

65

(Above) A heavy metal screen was located under the rear deck. The screen was unlatched and lowered for maintenance.

(Left) The two engine air filter canisters were located under the corners of rear hull overhang. Both were easily accessible from outside the vehicle. These filters are the more common square type. A second type — in a round canister — was less common.

(Below) Looking up under the rear hull overhang reveals the exhausts protruding down through a protective screen. The access door to the engine compartment is at the bottom. The right exhaust has a baffle arrangement.

(Above) The M4A3 was powered by an 8-cylinder, liquid-cooled Ford GAA gasoline engine which developed 500 hp. The Ford GAA became the preferred American tank engine due to its compact design, power-to-weight ratio, and durability.

(Right) The radiator hoses were ganged into a single fitting before entering the water pump at the bottom rear of the engine block. Two magnetos are mounted above the water pump. The crankcase air breather is centered above the magnetos. The pipe running just above the air breather is a warm air duct leading from the exhaust manifolds to the carburetors. This duct was present on both ends of the engine.

(Below) The engine starter motor is mounted on the lower front right side of the engine block. The back of the engine held most of the engine driven accessories: the oil pump, water pump, and the twin magnetos.

The round fitting on the lower front of the engine is the clutch housing. The circular plate in its center is the clutch flange, which connected to the drive shaft. The small lever beneath the flange is the clutch release arm. The long housing underneath the engine block is the oil pan. The two pipes on top of the engine are coolant pipes leading to the radiator.

The fans pulled air into the engine compartment through the large screened hatches on the engine deck. The air was then sent through the radiators and then out the back of the vehicle. Fan driven air, combined with the exhaust, often kicked large amounts of sand and dust, which sometimes pinpointed the tank's position.

The smaller Ford GAA powerplant took up much less room in the Sherman's engine compartment than the R975 series radial engines. The engine coolant pipes were connected to the radiator via rubber hoses. The air intake manifold is nestled between the coolant pipes.

The two cooling fans were driven by differential units connected to the engine accessory drives via drive shafts mounted at a right angle to the engine. Thirty volt generators were mounted behind the fan drives. The left exhaust pipe is visible above the generator and beneath the accessory drive shaft.

Each cylinder head was covered by a camshaft cover. The rectangular plate in the middle of the camshaft cover protected the spark plugs. The camshaft also drove the fuel pump, the small cylindrical device beneath the coolant pipe. The oil dipstick is located just above the exhaust manifold. The M4A3 oil system held eight gallons (30.3 L) of oil

The air intake manifold sat on top of the two carburetors. Air was ducted from the forward air cleaners to the carburetors via the elbow pipe in the center of the manifold. Fuel tanks, holding a combined 168 gallons (635.9 L), surrounded the engine compartment.

The M4A3 can be easily identified by the twin engine hatch covers on the engine deck. These lift up and outward and — based on personal experience — are extremely heavy and difficult to open.

Cooling was not a problem with the M4A3, due to the large screened engine deck hatches. The baffles forced the air to move in a specific direction — improving cooling efficiency — rather than circulate in the hot engine compartment.

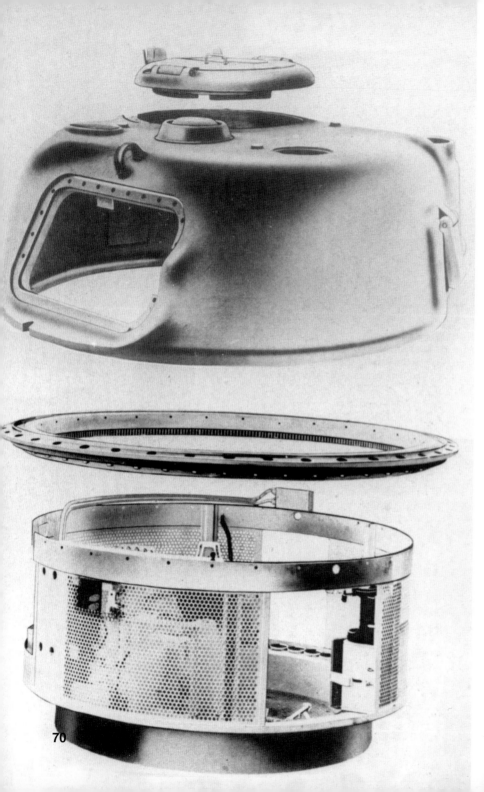

(Above) Looking down through the commander's cupola reveals the gunner's seat to the left with the triangular commander's seat behind it. The folding seat on the turret side is for the commander when the hatch is open. The boxes on the turret wall are part of the crew intercom system.

(Left) The M4 series was initially armed with the 75 mm M3 gun mounted in a cast turret with a partially enclosed turret basket. Ammunition was stored in the holes in the basket, visible through the opening on the right of the screen.

(Below) The gunner's station was equipped with controls to traverse the turret (the grip at right) and elevate the gun (the vertical hand wheel at left). The turret required a great deal of effort to turn any appreciable amount. These controls were used in the event of a power failure or to 'fine tune' the gun onto the target. The gunner's monocular sight is mounted above the elevation wheel.

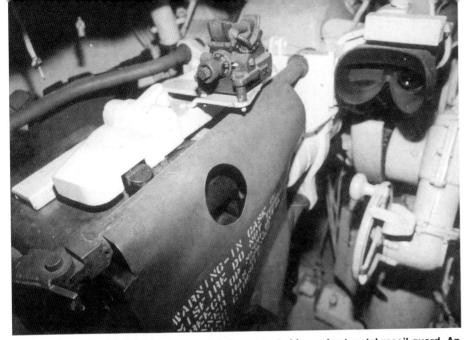

The gunner sat to the right of the gun and was protected by a sheet metal recoil guard. An M9 elevation quadrant is mounted on top of the recoil guard. The quadrant, used in conjunction with an azimuth indicator, allowed the gunner to lay the gun on an area target independent of the sights.

A co-axial .30 caliber M1919A4 machine gun was mounted to the left of the gun. This weapon moved with the main gun. The ammunition box and its holder are to the lower left of the machine gun. Above the machine gun is part of the main gun counterbalancing spring assembly.

The interior of this rebuilt M4A1 76 mm turret was generally similar to the 75 mm turret used on a 75 mm equipped M4A3. Both commander's seats are at the bottom while the gunner's seat at the top. To the left is the recoil guard and part of the 76 mm gun assembly.

The commander's seat is in the upright position for use when the tank is unbuttoned. Three of the six vision ports are visible above the seat. The boxes on the turret wall are part of the intercom system. Holders for binoculars and a flashlight are located adjacent to the seat.

The vehicle radio was mounted in the turret bustle. M4s carried either the SCR 508, 528, or 538 radio, which had a maximum range of up to twenty miles. This unit is the SCR 508, which was composed of a BC 604 Transmitter on the left and two BC 603 Receivers on the right — all mounted in a FT 237 base.

M4s were initially equipped with three different types of power controls for the turret and gun. This is the Oilgear system, by far the most common and reliable unit. The gun elevating hand wheel is at center left, while below the wheel is the cylindrical gyro stabilizer pump. The vertical black handle is the power traverse with the hand traverse handle to the right on top of the circular housing. The small box with the two dots at lower left contains the gun firing switches and the gun firing foot lever.

Headsets and microphones, part of the crew intercom system, were available at all crew positions in the tank. This headset is for the loader on the left side of the turret. The shell ejection port and its lever are just to the right of the microphone.

The gunner sat to the right of the gun. His seat, anchored to the bottom of the turret basket, turned with the turret. The gunner's M4A1 periscope in the upper right corner, while his telescopic sight is slightly below and to the left. Beneath the sight is the turret's power and manual control system.

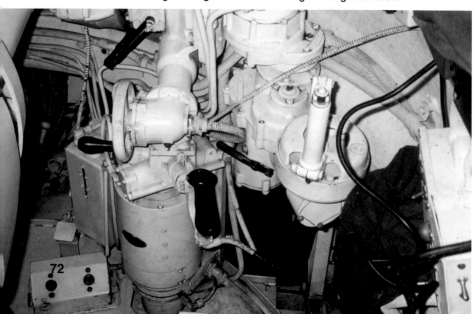

This M4A1 Sherman II was assigned to the HQ Company of the British 2nd Armoured Brigade in the Western Desert just prior to the second Battle of El Alamein. This is an early production M4 — characterized by the M3 Lee/Grant pattern VVSS suspension bogies.

The US 1st Armored Division operated this early production M4 in Italy during 1944. Most M4s were camouflaged in simple Olive Drab, however, several units took it upon themselves to add bands of red-brown and or sand yellow. Additionally, some Shermans had the lower hull sides and the underside of the gun barrel painted white to lessen the effects of dark shadows.

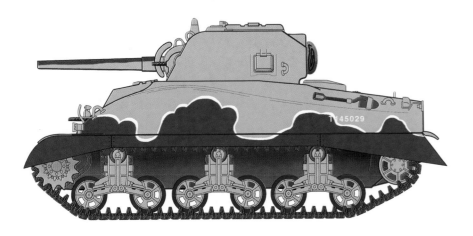

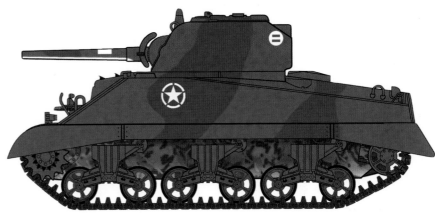

INTRUDER II, an M4 assigned to the US 2nd Armored Division in France during the summer of 1944, was an early production Sherman equipped with the 60° glacis plate and additional armor welded onto the hull sides. The white star on the hull side was painted out, since it was equivalent to a bull's eye to German anti-tank gunners.

ST QUENTIN was an early production M4A2 assigned to the French *1st Division Blindee, 4e Escadron, 1er Peloton* during the French march into Marseille in August of 1944. OPERATION ANVIL, the Allied invasion of southern France, began on 15 August 1944. By the end of the month, the French coastal ports had been seized and the Germans were pushed northward along the western face of the French Alps.

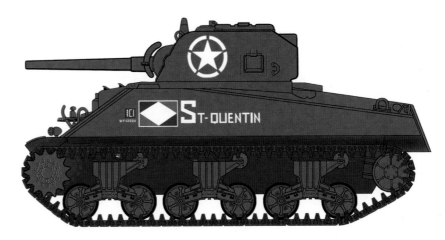

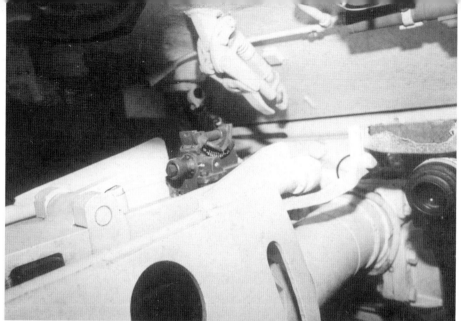

(Above) The 76 MM gun mount is similar to the mount used on the 75 MM gun. Above the M9 Elevation Quadrant is a locking mechanism to hold the gun mount stable during road movements. The telescopic gun sight is at the extreme right.

(Left) The gyro stabilizer pump, turret traverse motor, and the floor firing switches were mounted below the gunner's hand controls. The foot pedal was the primary means of firing the main gun, although the weapon could also be fired using electrical switches. The left button switch usually fired the co-axial .30 caliber machine gun.

(Below) The loader sat on the left side of the gun. His seat was attached to the turret ring and turned with the turret. Ammunition bins containing main gun rounds were set into the floor below the loader's position.

The canvas shell collection bag was fastened below the breech. The bag held several spent shell casing and kept them from littering the turret basket and possibly jamming the turret. The turret spotlight is stowed at the rear of the turret just under the covered radio set.

The gunner's seat is attached to the floor by four bolts and can be raised or lowered by the 'T' shaped grip on the bottom left of the unit. The handled released a small ratchet, visible in the second notch, and allowed the seat to be put into four possible positions.

The gunner's seat was attached to the turret basket floor and was adjustable in height. Directly above the seat beneath the binocular bracket is a flashlight operated off the tank's internal power.

The floor of the turret compartment contained most of the ammunition storage bins. A ready ammunition bin, visible at left, was attached to the turret basket. M4s equipped with the 76 MM gun carried 71 rounds of ammunition.

BATTLING BITCH was a cast hull M4A1 assigned to the 31st Battalion, 7th Armored Division in France. This tank retains its Cullin hedgerow cutters welded to the front transmission cover. BATTLING BITCH took part in the seizure of Chartres, France on 16 August 1944.

This M4 (105) Sherman was assigned to the 6th Armored Division in Luxembourg in January of 1945. Some M4s and M4A3s were equipped with 105 MM howitzers — a weapon more suited to destroying fixed defenses than the Sherman's usual 75 and 76 MM guns.

The US Marine Corps operated a large number of Shermans in the Pacific Theater. This M4A2 was assigned to the 3rd Tank Battalion on Iwo Jima in February of 1945. The tanks were often used to provide point blank fire into Japanese pillboxes and other fixed fortifications.

OLE MISS was a composite hull M4 assigned to B Company, 44th Tank Battalion in the Philippines in February of 1945. OLE MISS was in a 'Flying Column' which captured Santo Toman University in Manila.

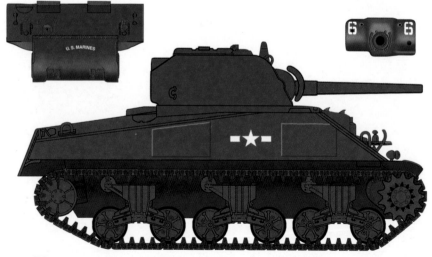

This M4A3E8 (76)W was assigned to the 14th Armored Division in Ohlungen, Germany in March of 1945. Sandbags, held in place by metal straps welded to the hull and turret, were used to increase the vehicle's protection against heavier German anti-tank guns. Black bands, used to break up the Sherman's outline, were sprayed directly over the bags.

DRAGON LADY was an early production welded hull M4 assigned to Company C of the 754th Tank Battalion in the Philippines during the Spring of 1945. DRAGON LADY carried a one-piece cast transmission cover.

WE GO/PAISAN was an M4A3E8 (76)W assigned to the 89th Tank Battalion, 8th Army on the Pusan Perimeter in August of 1950. Superior tactics and training enabled these Shermans to hold their own against the heavier gunned Russian T-434/85s.

TK2 was an M4A3E8 (105) assigned to the US Marines at the Chosin Reservoir, North Korea, in November of 1950. This 105 mm howitzer equipped Sherman also featured the fittings for a bulldozer blade attached to the glacis plate and running gear.

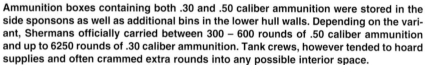

Ammunition boxes containing both .30 and .50 caliber ammunition were stored in the side sponsons as well as additional bins in the lower hull walls. Depending on the variant, Shermans officially carried between 300 – 600 rounds of .50 caliber ammunition and up to 6250 rounds of .30 caliber ammunition. Tank crews, however tended to hoard supplies and often crammed extra rounds into any possible interior space.

The rear of the T23 turret contains an SCR 528 radio. This unit was similar to the SCR 508, but only had a single BC 603 Radio Receiver (at right) instead of two. The BC 604 Radio Transmitter is located at left.

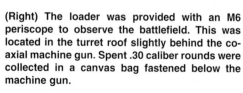

(Left) Most M4s had the main guns mounted on their sides. This allowed the breech block to slide horizontally away from the loader. The resulting space at the left and rear of the breech provided more room for the loader to chamber the round. This is a 76 MM gun in an M62 mount.

(Right) The loader was provided with an M6 periscope to observe the battlefield. This was located in the turret roof slightly behind the co-axial machine gun. Spent .30 caliber rounds were collected in a canvas bag fastened below the machine gun.

An internal turret azimuth indicator was mounted on the turret ring just behind the hand traverse mechanism. Combined with the M9 Elevation Quadrant, this allowed the gunner to recognize at a glance, the bearing and elevation of the main gun.

This ready ammunition rack held six rounds. Due to the larger size of the 76 MM shells only 71 rounds could be carried.

Most of the main gun ammunition was contained in floor storage bins equipped with hinged lids. Ten rounds, racked at an angle, could be stored in each bin.

Most of the ammunition bins were protected by quarter inch (6.3 MM) armor plate to protect them from shrapnel. The 'C' shaped handle allowed the gunner to pull the round out of the rack.

1168 AH-1 Cobra

1170 Fw 190

1171 de Havilland DH 2

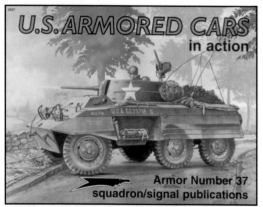

2037 U.S. Armored Cars

2038 U.S. Self-Propelled Guns

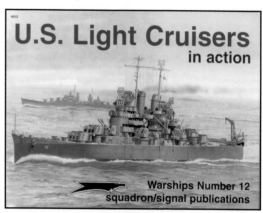

4012 U.S. Light Cruisers

5520 Space Shuttle

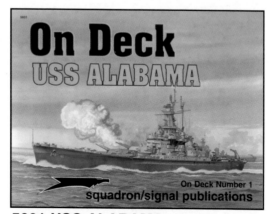

5601 USS ALABAMA

5521 F-86 Sabre